VOCAL SCORE

Made in England

THEATRE ROYAL, DRURY LANE

H. M. TENNENT LTD.

PRESENT

HERMAN LEVIN'S PRODUCTION

REX HARRISON · JULIE ANDREWS

MY FAIR LADY

ADAPTED FROM BERNARD SHAW'S "PYGMALION"

Produced on the screen by Gabriel Pascal

WITH

STANLEY HOLLOWAY

ROBERT COOTE ZENA DARE

MUSIC BY

FREDERICK LOEWE

BOOK AND LYRICS BY

ALAN JAY LERNER

PRODUCTION STAGED BY

MOSS HART

Choreography and Musical Numbers Staged by HANYA HOLM

Production Designed by OLIVER SMITH

Costumes Designed by CECIL BEATON

Musical Director CYRIL ORNADEL

Musical Arrangements by ROBERT RUSSELL BENNETT AND PHIL LANG

Lighting by JOE DAVIS

Dance Music Arranged by TRUDE RITTMAN

VOCAL SCORE

(Edited by FRANZ ALLERS)

PRICE 22/6

CHAPPELL & CO., LTD.
50 NEW BOND STREET, LONDON, W.1
CHAPPELL & CO., INC.
N.Y.C.

MADE IN ENGLAND

First performance at the Mark Hellinger Theatre, New York, March 15, 1956
First Performance in London at the
Theatre Royal, Drury Lane, April 30, 1958

MY FAIR LADY

THE CAST

(in order of appearance)

BUSKERS	JOAN ELVIN, TERRY WILLIAMS, WILLHELM MAURER
MRS. EYNSFORD-HILL	LINDA GRAY
ELIZA DOOLITTLE	JULIE ANDREWS
FREDDY EYNSFORD-HILL	LEONARD WEIR
COLONEL PICKERING	ROBERT COOTE
A BYSTANDER	MAX OLDAKER
HENRY HIGGINS	REX HARRISON
SELSEY MAN	ALAN DUDLEY
HOXTON MAN	REG TEMPLAR
ANOTHER BYSTANDER	BOB CHISHOLM
FIRST COCKNEY	ROBERT CRANE
SECOND COCKNEY	JOHN MOORE
THIRD COCKNEY	HOWARD DAVIES
FOURTH COCKNEY	ROBIN DUNBELL
BARTENDER	MOSTYN EVANS
HARRY	ALAN DUDLEY
JAMIE	BOB CHISHOLM
ALFRED P. DOOLITTLE	STANLEY HOLLOWAY
MRS. PEARCE	BETTY WOOLFE
MRS. HOPKINS	ELAINE GARREAU
BUTLER	JOHN MOORE
SERVANTS	HOWARD DAVIES, ELAINE LOVEGROVE, MARY BURGESS, FREDA SESSIONS, BRENDA GAYLE
MRS. HIGGINS	ZENA DARE
CHAUFFEUR	ALAN BURTON
FOOTMEN	PETER NEWTON, LEE KENTON
LORD BOXINGTON	ALAN DUDLEY
LADY BOXINGTON	ELAINE GARREAU
CONSTABLE	ALAN BURTON
FLOWER GIRL	CHARMIAN BURN
ZOLTAN KARPATHY	MAX OLDAKER
FLUNKEYS	WALLACE STEPHENSON, LEE KENTON
MAJOR DOMO	MOSTYN EVANS
QUEEN OF TRANSYLVANIA	MARGARET HALSTAN
AMBASSADOR	BOB CHISHOLM
BARTENDER	ROBERT CRANE
MRS. HIGGINS' MAID	WILLOW STOCKDALE

SINGING ENSEMBLE, DANCING ENSEMBLE

SYNOPSIS OF SCENES

The place is London. The time, 1912

ACT I

Scene 1. Outside the Opera House, Covent Garden—A cold March night
Scene 2. A Tenement Section, Tottenham Court Road—Immediately following
Scene 3. Higgins' Study—The following morning
Scene 4. A Tenement Section, Tottenham Court Road—Three days later
Scene 5. Higgins' Study—Later that day
Scene 6. Near the Race Meeting, Ascot—A July afternoon
Scene 7. Inside a Club Tent, Ascot—Immediately following
Scene 8. Outside Higgins' House, Wimpole Street—Later that afternoon
Scene 9. Higgins' Study—Six weeks later
Scene 10. The Promenade of the Embassy—Later that night
Scene 11. The Ballroom of the Embassy—Immediately following

ACT II

Scene 1. Higgins' Study—3 o'clock the following morning
Scene 2. Outside Higgins' House, Wimpole Street—Immediately following
Scene 3. Flower Market of Covent Garden—5 o'clock that morning
Scene 4. Upstairs Hall of Higgins' house—11 o'clock that morning
Scene 5. The Conservatory of Mrs. Higgins' house—Later that day
Scene 6. Outside Higgins' House, Wimpole Street—Immediately following
Scene 7. Higgins' Study—Immediately following

MY FAIR LADY

MUSICAL CONTENTS

ACT I

ACT II

MY FAIR LADY

FREDERICK LOEWE

No 1

OVERTURE AND OPENING SCENE

38
Brass
Tutti
Clar. Bsn.
52
Tempo giusto, brillante
f
60
Str. Hn.
mf
68
con calore

76
84
Più animato
Str.
poco accel.
f
92
100
f
mf
108
f più espressivo
poco allarg.

Moderato
Brass
mf cantabile
Vlns.
120 Allegretto
Str. W. W. 8va
sf
poco dim.
f molto cantabile
leggiero
128

W. W.
136
f add Brass
Hn.
144
poco rall.
a tempo
150
sfz
Brass
Pesante
Brass
The curtain rises
f
accel.
attacca

Act I

OPENING SCENE

43 Tempo di Soft Shoe
Clar.
mf
Fl. Ob. Vlns.
Brass
f accel.
59 Allegro molto
Vlns.
etc.
67
Poco meno
add Str. W. W.
rall.
Brass
75
a tempo
W. Bl.
Str. W. W.
poco accel.
(ELIZA)
Aoooooooow!
Dialogue continues

Chappell

No 2

SONG—(Higgins, with others)

"WHY CAN'T THE ENGLISH?"

ALAN JAY LERNER — FREDERICK LOEWE

Cue: HIGGINS: A woman who utters such depressing and disgusting sounds has no right to be anywhere— no right to live. Remember that you are a human being with a soul and the divine gift of articulate speech: that your native language is the language of Shakespeare and Milton and the Bible, and don't sit there crooning like a bilious pigeon.

(PICKERING) Come, sir, I think you picked a poor example.
(HIGGINS) Did I!
HIG
-ca-tion.
Brass
Cello
Bsn.
28 Vivo
Hear them down in So-ho Square, drop-ping aitch-es ev-'ry-where,
p Strs. Bsn.
Speak-ing Eng-lish an-y way they like.
Fl. Ob.
36 (To Cockney)
Cockney
You, sir, did you go to school? What-ya tike me fer, a fool?
Higgins
No- one taught him "take" in stead of "tike."

44
HIG
Hear a York-shire-man, or worse, Hear a Cor-nish - man con-verse. I'd ra - ther hear a
choir sing-ing flat!
Fl.Cl.
Meno mosso
Chick - ens cack-ling in a barn,
W.W.
56
(HIGGINS) Garn! I ask you, sir, what sort of word is that?
(ELIZA)
Just like this one, Garn! It's "Aooow" and "Garn" that keep her in her place,
Str.pizz.
Str.
p colla voce
Bsn.
L'istesso tempo
Not her wretched clothes and dirt-y face.
Why can't the Eng-lish teach their
f Brass
mp
child - ren how to speak? This verb - al class dis - tinc - tion by now should be an -

HIG
-tique. If you spoke as she does, sir, in-stead of the way you do, Why,
Wood Block
Wood Block
you might be sell-ing flow-ers too. An Eng-lish-man's way of
(PICKERING) I beg your pardon!
80
Cl.Bsn.
Ob.
speak-ing ab-so-lute-ly class-i-fies him. The mo-ment he talks he
makes some oth-er Eng-lish-man des-pise him. One com-mon lan-guage I'm a-
88
-fraid we'll nev-er get. Oh, why can't the Eng-lish learn to
Ob.Bsn.

96 L'istesso tempo
HIG
set a good ex - am - ple to peo - ple whose Eng - lish is pain - ful to your
leggiero
Cello
ears?
The Scotch and the I - rish leave you close to tears.
107
There ev - en are plac - es where Eng - lish com - plete - ly dis - ap -
(Spoken) In America, they haven't used it for years!
- pears.
f
117
Why can't the Eng - lish teach their chil - dren how to speak? Nor - we - gians learn Nor -
mf Brass. W.W.

125
HIG
-we-gian; the Greeks are taught their Greek. In France ev - 'ry French-man knows his
(Spoken) The French never care what they do, actually, as long as they pronounce it properly.
lan-guage from "A" to "Zed" A-
mf
Bsn.
131
-ra - bi - ans learn A - ra-bian with the speed of sum - mer light - ning; The
p
He-brews learn it back-wards, which is ab - so - lute - ly fright-'ning. But
Brass sf
139
use prop - er Eng-lish, you're re - gard - ed as a freak.
Wood Block

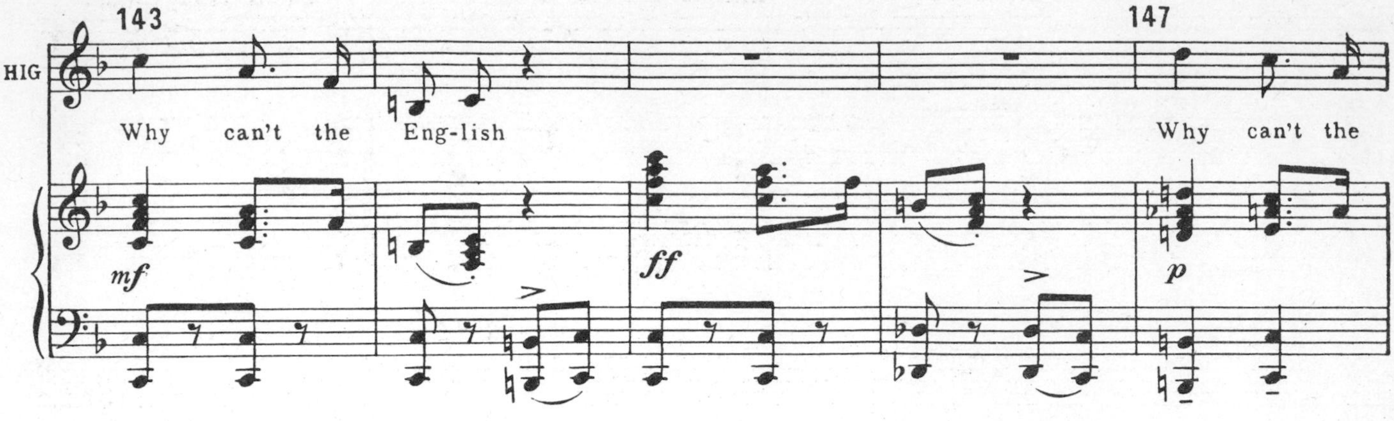

143
147
HIG
Why can't the Eng-lish
Why can't the
mf
ff
p

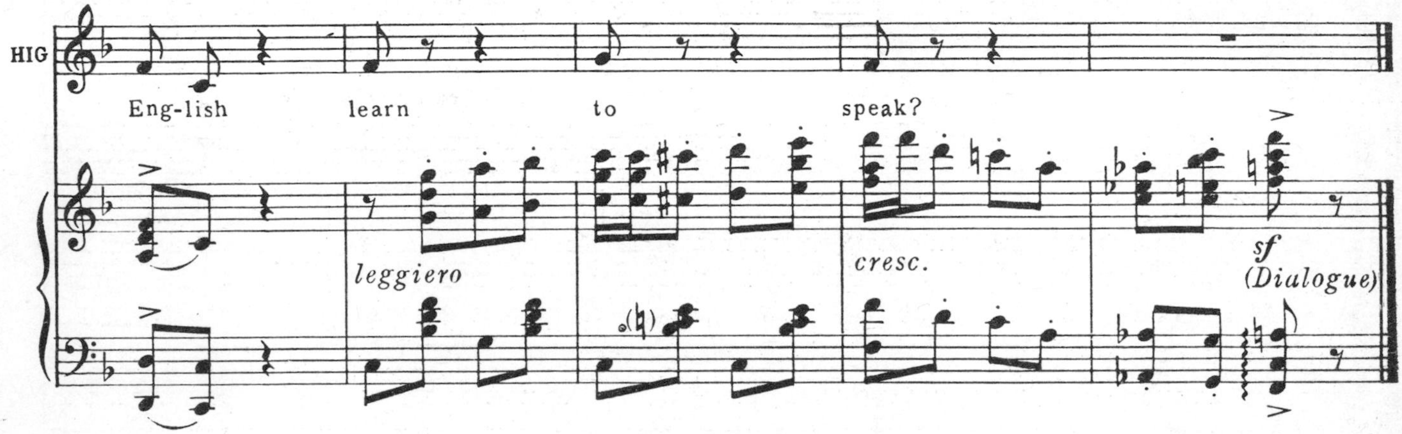

HIG
Eng-lish learn to speak?
leggiero
cresc.
sf
(Dialogue)

Nº 3 SONG — (Eliza & Male Chorus)

"WOULDN'T IT BE LOVERLY"

Cue: HIGGINS: Ah. The church. A reminder. *(Throwing some coins into Eliza's basket)* Indian dialects have always fascinated me. I have records of over fifty.

PICKERING: Have you, now? Did you know there are over two hundred?

ELIZA: Aooow!

ELIZA: Aooow!
Aoooow!
Aooooow!
f
Str.
W.W.

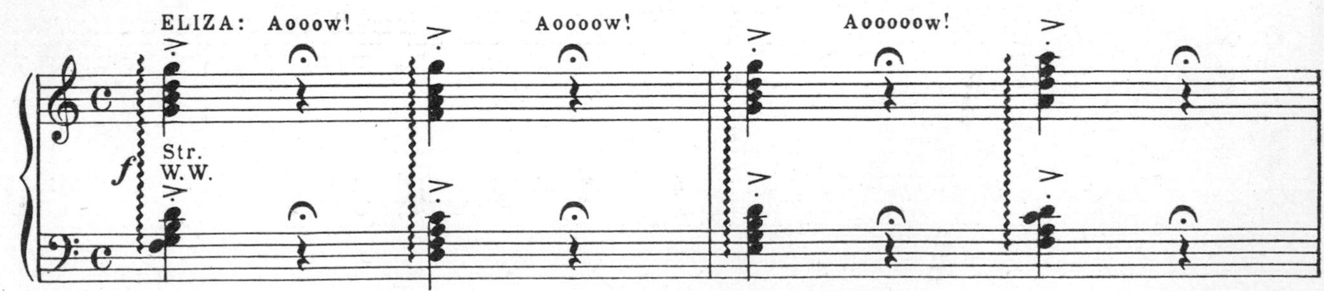

Moderato

1st COCKNEY: Shouldn't you stand up, gentlemen? We've got a bloomin' heiress in our midst.

Fl.
p

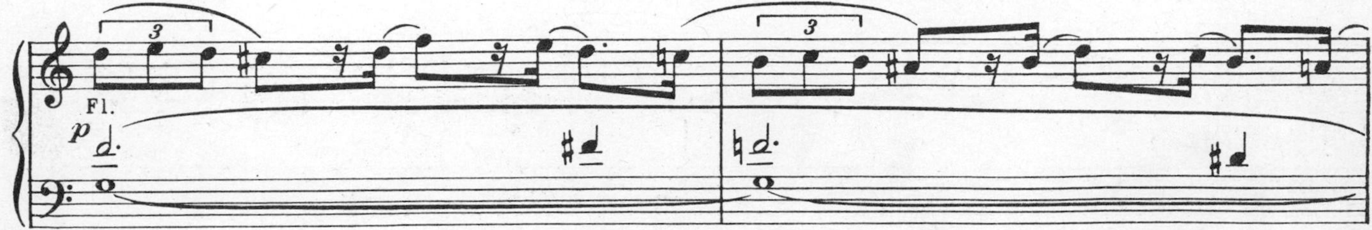

2nd COCKNEY: Would you be lookin' for a good butler, Eliza?

ELIZA: You won't do.

2nd Cockney (Bass)

It's

8 **Quasi recitativo**

3rd Cockney (Baritone)

rath - er dull in town; I think I'll take me to Pa - ree. Mmm

The

1st Cockney (Tenor)

mis - sus wants to o - pen up the cas - tle in Ca - pri. Mmm

Me

doc - tor rec - com - mends a qui - et sum - mer by the sea.

Moderato

Ten. I

Ten. II

p Mmm, Mmm, Would - n't it be lov - er - ly?

Bar.

Bass

3rd COCKNEY: Where're ya bound this spring, Eliza — Biarritz?

Clars.

pp leggiero

20 Eliza
All I want is a room some-where; Far a-way from the cold night air.
p Str.
ELIZ
With one e-nor-mous chair; oh, would-n't it be lov-er-ly?
28
Lots of choc-'late for
me to eat; Lots of coal mak-in' lots of heat; Warm face, warm hands, warm feet, oh,
Fl.
would-n't it be lov-er-ly?
31
Oh, so lov-er-ly sit-tin' ab-so-bloom-in'-
Fl. Clar.
3
-lute-ly still! I would nev-er budge 'til Spring crept
Clar. E. Hn.

44

ELIZ

o-ver me win-der-sill. Some-one's head rest-in' on my knee; warm and ten-der as

Hp. Str. Fl. Clar. obbl.

mf dolce

ELIZ

he can be, Who takes good care of me; oh, would - n't it be

52

ELIZ

lov - er - ly? Lov - er - ly! Lov - er - ly! Lov - er - ly! Lov - er - ly!

p W.W. Str. W.W. *rall.* Str. Str. W.W. *mf accel.*

58

Ten. I

Ten. II

CHO.

Ah, ———— Ah, ————

Bar.

Bass

All I want is a room some - where; Far a - way from the cold night air.

a tempo

Eliza
66
Oh, would - n't it be lov - er - ly? Lots of choc-'late for
CHO
With one e - nor - mous chair; Ah, Lots of choc-'late
With one e - nor - mous chair; Ah, Lots of choc-'late
Fl.
etc.
ELIZ
me to eat; Lots of coal mak - in' lots of heat. Warm face, warm hands, warm feet; Oh,
CHO
me eat; Lots of coal make lots heat. Warm face, warm hands, warm feet.
me eat; Lots of coal make lots heat. Warm face, warm hands, warm feet.
Fl.
74
ELIZ
would - n't it be lov - er - ly? Oh, so lov - er - ly sit - tin' ab - so - bloom - in'-
Solo Tenor pp
Ah, Ah Ah
Fl.
etc.

ELIZ: -lute - ly still! I would nev - er budge 'til Spring crept o - ver me win - der - sill.

S.T: O - ver me win - der,

82

ELIZ: Who takes good

CHO (All): Ah, Ah, Who takes good

Some - one's head rest - in' on my knee, Warm and ten - der as she can be, Who takes good

90

ELIZ: care of me, Oh, would - n't it be lov - er - ly? Lov - er - ly!

CHO: care of me, Ah, Lov - er - ly!

Lov - er - ly! Ah,

care of me, Ah, Ah,

W.W.

Str.

Str.

94
The men whistle as the sweepers dance
leggiero
Vlns.
etc.
Cl. Bsn.
mf
(Soft Shoe)
102
Vlns.
etc.
Cl. Bsn.
110
Muted Trpt.
p

118
Vlns.
etc.
Cl. Bsn.
mf
Eliza
126
Oh, would - - n't it be lov-er-ly?
Fl.
ELIZ
Lov-er-ly!
Lov-er-ly!
Ten. I
Ah,
Lov-er-ly!
Ah,
Lov-er-ly!
Ten. II
Barit.
Bass
Ah,
Ah,
CHO
(The scene changes)
Trpt.
Str.
Trpt.
W.W.
dim. poco a poco
Trbn.
Str.
pp
f
pizz.

No. 4 TRIO — (Doolittle, Jamie and Harry)

"WITH A LITTLE BIT OF LUCK"

Cue: DOOLITTLE: Goodnight, Eliza! You're a noble daughter! — You see, boys, I told you not to go home! It's just faith, hope and a little bit of luck!

Jamie
Harry
3
With a lit-tle bit, with a lit-tle bit,
With a lit-tle bit, with a lit-tle bit,
DOO
With a lit-tle bit, with a lit-tle bit,
With a lit-tle bit, with a lit-tle bit,
W.W.
f
Brass
JAM
HAR
With a lit-tle bit of luck, you'll nev - er work
With a lit-tle bit of luck, you'll give right in!
DOO
With a lit-tle bit of luck, you'll nev - er work
With a lit-tle bit of luck, you'll give right in!
1
2
Doolittle
DOO
The Lord a - Oh, you can walk the straight and nar - row;
W.W. Str. 8va
mf
DOO
but with a lit-tle bit of luck you'll run a - muck! The gen-tle
Trbn.
mf

C
DOO
sex was made for man to mar - ry To share his nest and
Hns.
see his food is cooked. The gen - tle sex was made for man to
mar - ry, but— With a lit - tle bit of luck, with a lit - tle bit of
Harp gliss.
pp
Jamie
Harry
With a
luck, You can have it all and not get hooked. With a
f
W.W.
f

ANGRY WOMAN: Shut your face down there! How's a woman supposed to get her rest?
DOOLITTLE: I'm tryin' to keep 'em quiet, lady!
ANGRY MAN: Shut up! Once and for all, shut up!

DOOLITTLE: 'Ere, 'ere — that's no way to talk to a lady! We've got to be neighbourly-like, boys.

JAM
HAR
with a lit-tle bit with a lit-tle bit of luck, you won't be home!
DOO
with a lit-tle bit with a lit-tle bit of luck, you won't be home!
They're al-ways throw - in' good - ness at you; But with a lit-tle bit of
W.W. Str. 8va
mf
luck, a man can duck! Oh, it's a crime for man to go phi-lan - d'rin'
C1
Hns.
Trbn.
And fill his wife's poor heart with grief and doubt. Oh, it's a

DOO
crime for man to go phi - lan - d'rin', but With a lit-tle bit of
Harp gliss.
pp
luck, With a lit-tle bit of luck, You can see the blood-hound don't find out!
f
Jamie
Harry
D1
With a lit-tle bit, with a lit-tle bit, With a
With a lit-tle bit, with a lit-tle bit, With a
f W.W.
Brass
JAM
HAR
E1
lit-tle bit of luck, she won't find out! With a lit-tle bit, with a
lit-tle bit of luck, she won't find out! With a lit-tle bit, with a
f Trbn.
ff W.W.
Brass

N.B. In the orchestra parts, the following number (4A) is not written out separately, but starts at a 𝄋 *(Bar 7 of page 27 in this score) in No. 4*

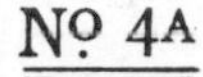

Nº 4A CHANGE OF SCENE

Moderato

Brass

Vln. W.W.

etc.

ff

Trbn.

mf Hn. Trbn.

Hn.

Harp gliss.

sfz

A voice is heard practicing vowel sounds. It continues in seemingly endless monotony. (The curtain rises)

No 5

SONG–(Higgins)

"I'M AN ORDINARY MAN"

Cue: HIGGINS: I find that the moment I let myself become friends with a woman. I become selfish and tyrannical. So here I am, a confirmed old bachelor, and likely to remain so. After all, Pickering:

doing what-ev-er he thinks is best for him. Just an or-di-nar-y man.
Cl.
p
grazioso
W.W.
But let a
14 Allegro molto vivo
wo-man in your life
Tutti
mf
f
And your se-ren-i-ty is through!
p
W.W. f
22
She'll re-dec-or-ate your
home From the cel-lar to the dome; Then get on to the en-thrall-ing fun of ov-er-haul-ing you.
W.W.
f L.H.
Oh, let a
p

34
HIG
wo-man in your life
And you are up a-gainst the wall!
(Trpt.)
42
Make a plan and you will find she has something else in mind; And so
ra-ther than do eith-er, you do some-thing else that nei-ther likes at all.
(W.W. Trpt.)
54 Più mosso
You want to talk of Keats or Mil-ton;
(Str.)
62
She on-ly wants to talk of love.
You go to see a

HIG
play or bal-let And spend it search-ing for her glove.
f p
70
Oh, let a wo-man in your life And you in-vite e-ter-nal
p f p
Molto meno 78
strife! Let them buy their wedding bands for those
(W.W.)
p (Vln. Solo)
(Str. W.W.)
A tempo
ten. ten.
an-xious lit-tle hands; I'd be e-qual-ly as will-ing for a dent-ist to be
ten. (Fl. Cl.)
mf
ten.
Pesante
Come prima
(Spoken)
drilling than to ev-er let a wo-man in my life!
I'm a very gentle
(Cl.)
f ff p

90 Calmato
HIG
man; Ev - en - tem - per'd and good-na - tur'd, whom you
add. Fl.
(Str.) scherzando
nev - er hear com - plain; — Who has the milk of hu - man kind - ness by the
quart in ev-'ry vein. A pa-tient man am I — down to my fin - ger-tips; — The sort who
97
nev - er could, ev - er would, Let an in - sult - ing re - mark es - cape his lips. —
(Cl.)
p
— Just a ve - ry gen - tle man. —
W.W.
But let a

 Chappell

103 Allegro vivo
HIG
wo-man in your life
And pa-tience has-n't got a chance.
111
She will beg you for ad - vice; your re - ply will be con -
-cise. And she'll lis-ten ve - ry nice-ly, then go out and do pre - cise-ly what she
wants!
W.W. Tpt.
123 Più mosso
You were a man of grace and
pol - ish, Who nev-er spoke a - bove a hush
Now all at
mf
f
p
f
p
f
p
f
p

131
HIG
once you're us - ing lan-guage that would make a sail - or blush
139
Oh, let a wo-man in your life And you are plung-ing in a
knife!
W. W.
Molto meno 149
Let the oth-ers of my sex tie the
(Str. W. W.)
knot a-round their necks; I'd pre - fer a new e - di-tion of the Span-ish In-qui -
ten. ten.
A tempo
(Fl. Cl.)
-si-tion Than to ev-er let a wo-man in my life!
Pesante
Come prima
(Spoken)
I'm a quiet living
(Cl.)

161
HIG
man
Who pre-fers to spend his ev-'nings in the
W.W.
(Str.)
si-lence of his room. Who likes an at-mos-phere as rest-ful as an
un-dis-cov-er'd tomb. A pen-sive man am I of phil-o-soph-ic joys; Who likes to
med-i-tate, con-tem-plate, free from hu-man-i-ty's mad, in-hum-an
add Ob.
noise. Just a qui-et living man. But let a
L.H.
p (Trom.)
pp
Trpt.

174 Allegro vivo
HIG
wo-man in your life
And your sab - ba - ti - cal is
mf
f
p
through!
Trpt.
182
In a line that nev - er ends come an
ar - my of her friends, Come to jab - ber and to chat - ter and to tell her what the
mat - ter is with you.
She'll have a
Brass
p

HIG
boom - ing, boist - 'rous fam - 'ly Who will de - scend on
you en masse. She'll have a large Wag - ner - ian
moth - er With a voice that shat - ters glass!
(A gibberish of voices begins as he turns on a phonograph)
210
Oh, let a wo-man in your life, Let a
(Str.W.W.)
Brass

(... And another phonograph)
HIG
wo-man in your life,
Let a wo-man in your life.
f
p
mf
220
(The sound of voices rises over the orchestra)
cresc.
poco
228
a
poco
cresc.
cresc. molto
(He turns off the phonographs)
Slowly
Higgins
I shall nev-er let a wo-man in my
sff
Bsn.
p
Str.
Presto
(Curtain)
HIG
life.
f
attacca

Chappell

No. 5a.

CHANGE OF SCENE

Nº 6 REPRISE—(Doolittle and Chorus)

"WITH A LITTLE BIT OF LUCK"

Cue: DOOLITTLE: I knowed she had a career in front of her! Harry, boy, we're in for a booze-up. The sun is shinin' on Alfred P. Doolittle

mf
CHO
lit-tle bit, With a lit-tle bit of luck, they'll work for you. He does-n't
mf
lit-tle bit, With a lit-tle bit of luck, they'll work for you. He does-n't
C
cresc sempre
CHO
have a tuppence in his pock - et; The poor-est bloke you'll ev-er hope to
cresc sempre
have a tup-pence in his pock - et; The poor-est bloke you'll ev-er hope to
W.W.
Brass
mf
fz
pp
CHO
meet. He does-n't have a tup-pence in his pock - et, but — With a
fz
meet. He does-n't have a tup-pence in his pock - et, but
Str.
pp
fz

f
CHO
pp
lit - tle bit of luck, With a lit - tle bit of luck, He'll be mov - in' up to
f
lit - tle bit of luck, With a lit - tle bit of luck, He'll be mov - in' up to
f add W.W. Hn.
D
CHO
eas - y street. With a lit - tle bit, with a
eas - y street. With a lit - tle bit, with a
Brass
CHO
lit - tle bit, With a lit - tle bit of luck, he's mov - in' up.
lit - tle bit, With a lit - tle bit of luck, he's mov - in' up.
f

CHO
With a lit-tle bit, with a lit-tle bit, with a
With a lit-tle bit, with a lit-tle bit, with a
W.W.
CHO
lit-tle bit of bloom-in' luck!
lit-tle bit of bloom-in' luck!
E
Doolittle dances with the crowd
Vln.W.W.
etc.
Brass
Trbn.
Brass
Hp.gliss.

G
ff
With a lit-tle bit, with a
lit-tle bit, With a lit - tle bit of bloom - in' luck!
CHO
W.W.
f
Curtain
attacca
N.B: In the orchestra parts, the following number (6A) is not written out separately, but starts at a 𝄋 (one bar before Ⓔ, page 45 in this score) in Nº 6
Nº 6a.
CHANGE OF SCENE
Moderato
Vln.W.W.
Brass
etc.
Trbn.
mf Hn Trbn.
W.W.
Hp.gliss.
(The curtain rises)
Dialogue
sfz

Nº 7

SONG—(Eliza)

"JUST YOU WAIT"

Cue: HIGGINS: Eliza, I promise you you will pronounce the letter "a" correctly before this day is out, or there'll be no lunch, no dinner, and no chocolates!

Eliza slams her study book down on the floor

Chappell

ELIZ

scream to fetch a doc-tor doub-le quick! I'll be off a sec-ond la - ter, And go

Trbn. *p* Str. Ob.

ELIZ

straight to the the - a - tre! Oh, ho ho, 'en - ry 'ig - gins, just you wait.

19

ELIZ

Ooooooh, 'en - ry 'ig - gins! Just you wait un - til we're swim-min' in the

Trpt. *sf>p*

ELIZ

sea! Ooooooh, 'en - ry 'ig-'gins And you

Trpt. Bsn. *sf>p*

ELIZ

get a cramp a lit - tle ways from me! When you yell you're gon-na drown, I'll get

29

LIZ: dressed and go to town! Oh, ho, ho, 'en - ry 'ig-gins! Oh, ho, ho, 'en - ry 'ig - gins!

Trbn. *f* Trpts.

LIZ: Just you wait! One___

ff Str. *p* *poco rit.* Fl.

Amabile

LIZ: day I'll be fam - ous! I'll be pro - per and prim! Go to

Bsn. Harp *simile*

LIZ: Saint James so oft - en I will call it Saint Jim. One eve - ning the King will say, "Oh,

LIZ: Li - za, old thing, I want all of Eng - land your prai - ses to sing. Next

Str.

42
ELIZ
week, on the twen-ti-eth of May, I pro - claim Li - za Doo - lit-tle
pp Str.
Trpt.
mf
Vln.
mf
Day! All the peo - ple will cel - e - brate the glo - ry of you, And what-
Fl.
pp
Bsn. Harp
simile
-ev - er you wish and want I glad - ly will do. "Thanks a
lot, King," says I, in a man - ner well bred; "But all I want is 'en-ry 'ig-gins
pp
poco rit.
54
Poco più mosso
'ead!" "Done," says the King, "with a stroke.
f a tempo
mf Str.
Trpt. W.W.

LIZ
Guard, run and bring— in the bloke!" Then they'll
ff
mf
58 Allegro marziale
march you 'en - ry 'ig - gins, to the wall; And the
Brass
king will tell me: "Li - za, sound the call." As they raise their ri-fles high-er, I'll shout:
"Rea-dy! Aim! Fire!" Oh, ho, ho! 'en - ry 'ig - gins! Down you'll
f
Trbn.
Tutti
sfz
muffled Dr.
Curtain
go! 'en - ry 'ig-gins! Just you wait!
sfz
ff

No 8

CHORUS– (with Higgins and Eliza)

"POOR PROFESSOR HIGGINS"

Cue: ELIZA: Ha-ha-ha-ha....
HIGGINS: Go on! Go on!

The stage darkens. Six servants are seen at one side of the stage

HIGGINS: (*Spoken*) *He plays Xylophone* *Dialogue continues*

Kind of you, *kind* of you. How kind of you to let me come.

Bsn. *p*

Cue: HIGGINS: Oh, it won't go to waste. I know someone who's immensely fond of strawberry tarts.
ELIZA: Aaaooowww!

The servants appear

22 **Più mosso** *legato*

CHO

Poor__ Pro-fes-sor Higgins!__ Poor__ Pro-fes-sor Higgins!__

legato

Più mosso Poor__ Pro-fes-sor Higgins!__ Poor__ Pro-fes-sor Higgins!__

Strg. Xyl. *poco f* Trpt. *p*

On he plods, against all odds; Oh, poor_ Professor Higgins! 31 Nine P. M., Ten P. M., On through midnight

On he plods, against all odds; Oh, poor_ Professor Higgins! Nine P. M., Ten P. M., On through midnight

cresc. poco *mf* *subito p*

(*The servants disappear*) HIGGINS: Four, Five, Six marbles. *Dialogue continues*

ev-'ry night. One A. M., Two A. M., Three.

ev-'ry night. One A. M., Two A. M., Three.

dim. *pp*

Horn Bsn.

Cue: HIGGINS: ...What's the matter? Why did you stop?
ELIZA: I Swallowed one.
HIGGINS: Oh, don't worry. I have plenty more. Open your mouth... One, two, three, four....
(Again the servants are seen)

Nº 9 TRIO– (Eliza, Higgins and Pickering)

"THE RAIN IN SPAIN"

Cue: HIGGINS: Now, try it again.
ELIZA: The rain in Spain stays mainly in the plain.
HIGGINS: What was that?
ELIZA: The rain in Spain stays mainly in the plain.
HIGGINS: Again.
ELIZA: The rain in Spain stays main - ly in the plain. HIGGINS: I think she's got it! I think she's

Eliza, Higgins and Pickering
19
ELIZ
Spain! In Spain! The rain in Spain stays main - ly in the
mf
ALL
plain! The rain in Spain stays main - ly in the
f Brass
mf
Higgins
27 Poco più mosso
ALL
plain! In Hert-ford, Her - e-ford and Hamp-shire?
Cl.
f
p
Strg.
Eliza
He plays Xylophone
Eliza (Spoken)
Hur-ri-canes hard-ly hap-pen. How kind of you to
W.W.
mf
Vln. Solo
p
Higgins
35
Eliza
ELIZ
let me come. Now, once a - gain, where does it rain? On the plain! On the
Strg.
mf

Higgins
Eliza
ELIZ
plain! And where's that blas - ted plain? In Spain! In
p
f
Eliza, Higgins and Pickering
43 Ancora più animato
Spain! The rain in Spain stays main - ly in the plain!
ff Tutti
mf
ALL
The rain in Spain stays main - ly in the plain!
50 They dance an impromptu Spanish fandango
ff brillante
Tutti
meno f

58
Jota
65 (con fuoco)
cresc.
ff sempre
3
77
ALL THREE: O - le!
8va
(Dialogue)
sfz
sfz

Nº 10 SONG—(Eliza,)(with 1st & 2nd Maids and Mrs. Pearce)

"I COULD HAVE DANCED ALL NIGHT"

Cue: Mrs. PEARCE: You've all been working much too hard. I think the strain is beginning to show. Eliza, I don't care what Mr. Higgins says, you must put down your books and go to bed.

14
ELIZ
danced all night! I could have danced all night And
Fl., Cl.
etc.
still have begged for more. I could have
22
spread my wings And done a thou - - sand things I've
Fl., Cl.
etc.
nev - - er done be - fore. I'll nev-er
Hn., Bsn.
30
know what made it so ex - cit - - ing; Why all at
Vln. pizz.
etc.
Fl.

ten. ten. ten.
once my heart took flight. I on-ly
ten. ten. ten.
Str.
ten. ten. ten.
38
know when he be-gan to dance with me, I could have danced, danced,
a tempo
45 L'istesso tempo
danced, All night!
Trpt.
mp
Trpt.
mf
Eliza
I could have
1st Maid
2nd Maid
Both
It's af-ter three, now. Don't you a-gree, now, She ought to be in bed?
Harp
Hn.
p
muted Tpt.
p sempre

53
ELIZ
danced all night! I could have danced all
1st Maid
You're tired out.
2nd Maid
You must be dead.
1st Maid
Your face is drawn.
W. W.
ELIZ
night! And still have begged for
2nd Maid
Your eyes are red.
Both
Now say good-night, please. Turn out the light, please.
ELIZ
more. I could have
BOTH
It's real-ly time for you to be in bed.

61
ELIZ
spread my wings And done a thou - - - sand
1st Maid
Do come a-long, do as you're told.
2nd Maid
Or Mrs. Pearce
etc.
ELIZ
things I've nev - - - er done be -
2nd M
is apt to scold.
Both
You're up too late, miss, And sure as fate miss,
ELIZ
-fore. I'll nev-er know what made it
BOTH
You'll catch a cold.
Str.
p sempre
ELIZ
so ex - cit - - ing; Why all at

ELIZ
ten. ten. ten.
once my heart took flight. I on - ly
ten. ten. ten.
f
ten. ten. ten.
77
know when he be - gan to dance with
1st Maid
Put down your book.
2nd Maid
The work -'ll keep.
Both
Now set - tle down
a tempo
cresc.
me, I could have danced, danced, danced, all
BOTH
And go to sleep.
f
p

84 **Poco meno**

ELIZ: night! ___

Mrs. Pearce: I un-der-stand, dear. It's all been grand, dear. But now it's time to sleep.

Tempo I

Tutti *mf* *dim.* *pp*

Eliza *pp* I could have

92

ELIZ: danced all night! ___ I could have danced all night! And

ELIZ: still have begged for more. ___ I could have

Fl., Ob.

100
ELIZ
spread my wings ___ And done a thou - sand things I've
nev - - er done be - fore. ___
Fl.
W.W.
108
I'll nev - er know ___ what made it so ex -
Hn. Bsn.
cresc.
poco
etc.
a
-cit - ing; ___ Why all at once my
poco

116
LIZ
heart took flight. I on - ly know when
mf a tempo
crescendo
he be-gan to dance with me I could have danced, danced,
f
danced all night
Curtain
f
ff attacca
No. 10A
CHANGE OF SCENE
Capriccioso
Trpt.
mf
The curtain rises

No. 11

CHORUS
"ASCOT GAVOTTE"

Cue: Mrs HIGGINS: Charles, you'd better stay close to the car. I may be leaving abruptly.

CHO
smash-ing, pos-i-tive-ly dash-ing spec-ta-cle-the As-cot op-'ning day. At the
Smash-ing, pos-i-tive-ly dash-ing spec-ta-cle-the As-cot op-'ning day. At the
W.W.
24
gate are all the hor-ses wait-ing for the cue to fly a-way. What a
gate are all the hor-ses wait-ing for the cue to fly a-way. What a
dolce
Str.
grip-ping, ab-so-lute-ly rip-ping mo-ment at the As-cot op-'ning day.
grip-ping, ab-so-lute-ly rip-ping mo-ment at the As-cot op-'ning day.
mf
Str.
p

32
CHO
Pul-ses rush-ing! Fa-ces flush-ing!
Pul-ses rush-ing! Fa-ces flush-ing!
Fl., Ob.
5
5
mf
Heart-beats speed up! I have nev-er been so keyed up!
Heart-beats speed up! I'm so keyed up!
W.W.
Str.
40
cresc.
An-y sec-ond now they'll be-gin to run. Hark! A bell is ring-ing, they are
cresc.
An-y sec-ond now they'll be-gin to run. Hark! A bell is ring-ing, they are
p cresc.
poco a
2
4

There is complete silence. With nerveless faces the spectators watch the progress of the race. When it is over, they sing:
pp
mf
CHO
spring-ing for-ward Look! It has be-gun! What a
Racing Bell
poco
mf
pp
lunga
mf
46
fren-zied mo-ment that was! Did-n't they main-tain an ex-haust-ing pace? 'Twas a
Tutti
espr.
thrill-ing, ab-so-lute-ly chill-ing run-ning of the As-cot op-'ning race!
f
Tutti

54 The crowd moves to the strains of the Gavotte
sempre grazioso
Cello, Hn. Bsn.
62
marcato
Cello
Trbn.
Trpt. muted
mf
f
Strgs.
Hn.
70
mf
cantato
p
f
78
sempre grazioso

Nº 12 END OF SCENE — (Ensemble)

Cue: ELIZA: Have I said anything I oughtn't?
Mrs. HIGGINS: Not at all, my dear.
ELIZA: Well, that's a mercy, anyhow. What I always say is...
PICKERING: I don't suppose there's enough time before the next race to place a bet?

FREDDY: I have a bet on number seven. I should be so happy if you would take it. You'll enjoy the race ever so much more.

ELIZA: That's very kind of you. FREDDY: His name is Dover.

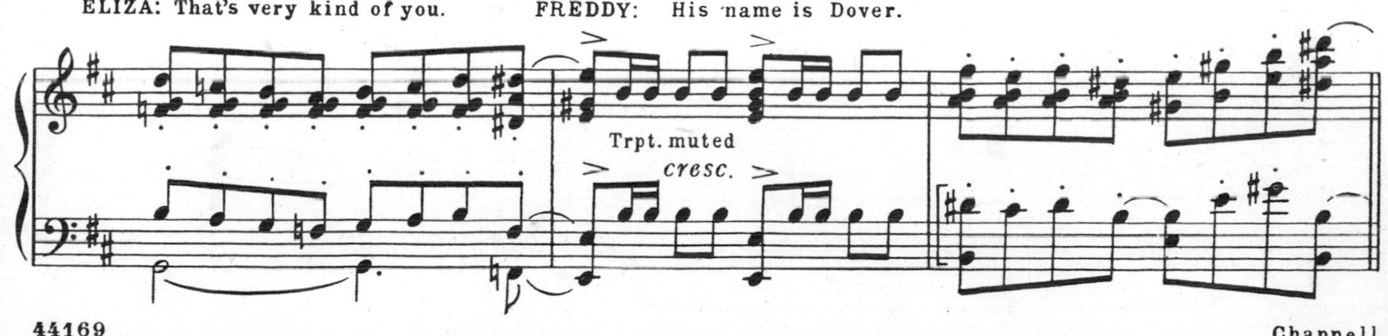

9 Soprano
mp cresc.
Alto
CHO
There they are a-gain, Lin-ing up to run, Now they're hold-ing stead-y they are
Tenor mp cresc.
Bass
There they are a-gain, Lin-ing up to run, Now they're hold-ing stead-y they are
p
cresc.
Again complete silence. The one exception is Eliza
ELIZA: Come on, come on, Dover..... Come on, Dover!!! Move your bloomin' arse!!!!
pp
ready-y for it-- Look! It has be-gun!
pp
ready-y for it-- Look! It has be-gun!
Racing Bell
pp
lunga
Allegro molto con brio
ff
Tutti
(Blackout)
ff
(The curtain rises)

Nº 13 SONG — (Freddy, with Mrs. Pearce)

"ON THE STREET WHERE YOU LIVE"

Cue: FREDDY: Officer, I know this is Wimpole Street, but could you tell me where 27-A is?
POLICEMAN: Right there, sir
FREDDY: Thank you.... Are those for sale?
FLOWER GIRL: Yes, sir. A shilling

FREDDY: Is Miss Doolittle at home?
Mrs. PEARCE: Whom shall I say is calling?
Mrs. Pearce
FRED
mo-ment when she shout-ed, "Move your bloom-in'." Yes, sir?
rall.
pp
Str.
a tempo
FREDDY: Freddy Eynsford-Hill. If she doesn't remember me, tell her I'm the chap who was sniggering at her.
Mrs. PEARCE: Yes, sir.
FREDDY: And would you give her these?
poco rit.
21 Allegro moderato
Mrs. PEARCE: Yes, sir.
FREDDY: You needn't rush. I want to drink in this street where she lives.
Mrs. PEARCE: Yes, sir.
Freddy
I have
Str. W.W.
p
add Cl. Bsn.
p con tenderezza
27 Tempo giusto
FRED
of - ten walked down this street be - fore; But the pave-ment al - ways
Cello
FRED
stayed be-neath my feet be - fore. All at once am I sev-'ral sto-ries high,
35
p sempre

Chappell

43

FRED

Know-ing I'm on the street where you live. Are there li-lac trees

Cls.

Cello

FRED

in the heart of town? Can you hear a lark in an-y oth-er

51

FRED

part of town? Does en-chant-ment pour out of ev-'ry door? No, it's

Cls.

59

FRED

just on the street where you live. And oh, the tow-er-ing

Vln.

poco cresc.

mf

FRED

feel-ing Just to know some-how you are near! The

Cello

Bsn.

67
FRED
o - - ver-pow-er-ing feel - ing That an-y sec-ond you may sud-den-ly ap-
3
- pear! Peo-ple stop and stare. They don't both-er me, For there's
75
Ob.espr.
p
Cello
no-where else on earth that I would rath-er be. Let the time go by; I won't
83
ten.
poco cresc.
care if I Can be here on the street where you live.
ten. ten.
mf
Cl.
pp Str.
Mrs.PEARCE: Mr. Eynsford-Hill? FREDDY: Yes. Mrs. PEARCE: I'm terribly sorry, sir. Miss Doolittle says she doesn't want to see anyone ever again.
91
Cello

FREDDY: But why? She was magnificent!
Mrs. PEARCE: Magnificent? Do you have the right address, sir?
FREDDY: Of course. Tell her I'll wait.
Mrs. PEARCE: But it might be days, sir.
99
Even weeks! FREDDY: But don't you see? I'll be happier here.
Freddy (Sings)
107
Cls.
Strs.
p sub.
Cello
People stop and stare. They don't bother me. For there's nowhere else on earth that I would rather be.
FRED
115
cresc.
Let the time go by, I won't care if I Can be here on the street where you live.
CURTAIN
Str. W.W.
f a tempo
Hn.
Brass
ff

No 14 ELIZA'S ENTRANCE

Cue: PICKERING: .... What of the girl? You act as if she doesn't matter at all.
HIGGINS: Rubbish, Pickering. Of course she matters. What do you think I've been doing all these months? What could possibly matter more than to take a human being and change her into a different human being by creating a new speech for her? Why, it's filling up the deepest gulf that separates class from class and soul from soul. She matters immensely.

(Higgins pours a glass of port..... downs it quickly.)
Str.
mf
25
W.W.
etc.
cresc.
(Higgins offers Eliza his arm.)
(They start off together)
(Curtain)
sfz>mf<ff
Brass
attacca
End of Act I
ENTRACT (18)
Nº 15
INTRODUCTION TO PROMENADE
32
Moderato
f Str. Brass
Tutti
(Two footmen enter in front of the curtain.)
40
W.W.
etc.
(They exit, opening the curtain.)
Segue

Nº 16 PROMENADE

PICKERING:
Mrs. Higgins!
MRS. HIGGINS:
Excuse me.
(Dialogue continues)
100
pp
108
poco rit.
Molto moderato
114
Cl.
sempre pp
PICKERING:
Mrs. Higgins, do you think Eliza will make it?
MRS. HIGGINS:
Oh, I hope so! I've grown terribly
fond of that girl.
FOOTMAN:
Professor Henry Higgins.
KARPATHY: Ah, Maestro, Maestro!
(Dialogue continues)

No. 17

EMBASSY WALTZ

Mrs. **HIGGINS:** Henry, do you think it wise to stay
HIGGINS: Stay? Why not?
FOOTMAN: Miss Eliza Doolittle.
KARPATHY: Ah, Professor you must introduce me...

47 *Higgins and Eliza disappear into the swirl and reappear from time to time.*

Fl.

W.W.

Tutti

55

etc.

W. W. Str.

63

Cello
Trbn.

add Trpt.

71

A la Viennoise

ff

Tutti

79

f marc.

87 Fl. etc.

f cantabile

94

ff

102

f cantabile

Ancora ben tenuto 109

mf *cresc.*

sf *a tempo*

Fl.Cl.

(Bell)

117

Fl.Cl.

(Bell)

125

Karpathy gets closer and closer to Eliza

f cantato

End of Act I

Chappell

Nº 18 ENTR'ACTE

35
Fl. Bells
p
f Strs. W.W.
47 Vivo
Trpt.
51 Allegro moderato
f
f

59
Str.
mf
67
Fl.
p
Tutti
75
cresc. poco a poco
L.H.
ff

(𝅗𝅥 = ♩) Con brio
Molto allegro
90 Str. W.W.
ff Brass
Str.W.W. 102
sfz
mf
ff Trbn.
110
mf

122
Più agitato
cresc.
Trbn.
134
poco
a
poco
cresc.
Trbn.
Allegro brilliante
(♩=𝅗𝅥)
146
sf
ff ben tenuto
sf
Tempo I
153
ff
157
accel.
sf attacca

Chappell

Act II

Nº 19

DUET (Higgins and Pickering) and Chorus

"YOU DID IT"

PICKERING: Absolutely fantastic.
HIGGINS: A lot of tomfoolery.
PICKERING: Higgins, I salute you.
HIGGINS: Nonsense, the silly people don't know their own silly business.
34
Pickering
43
To - night, old man you did it! You did it! You did it! You said that you would do it, And in - deed you did. I
poco cresc.
mf
mp
Str. W.W.
PIC
51
thought that you would rue it; I doubt-ed you'd do it. But now I must ad - mit it That suc-ceed you did.
59
You should get a med-al, Or be e - ven made a

Higgins
Pickering 67
PIC
knight. It was noth-ing. Real-ly noth-ing. All a-lone you
Vln.
etc.
Higgins
hurdled ev-'ry ob-sta-cle in sight. Now, wait! Now, wait! Give cred-it where it's
Hp.
Pickering 79
HIG
due: A lot of the glo-ry goes to you. But you're the one who
poco
did it Who did it Who did it. As stur-dy as Gib-ral-tar, Not a sec-ond did you
cresc.
poco
a
poco
mf
87
fal-ter, There's no doubt a-bout it, You did it!
Vln. Fl.
cresc.
f

Chappell

Meno mosso
95 Soft Shoe tempo
PIC
I must have aged a year to-night. At
W.W.
times I thought I'd die of fright. Nev-er was there a mo-men-ta-ry lull.
Higgins
Brass
Short-ly af-ter we came in, I
HIG
saw at once we'd eas-'ly win, And af-ter that I found it dead-ly
Pickering
103
dull. You should have heard the ooh's and ah's;
Brass

Higgins

PIC

Ev-'ry-one won-d'ring who she was. You'd think they'd nev-er seen a la-dy be-

Pickering

HIG

-fore. And when the Prince of Tran-syl-va-nia asked to meet her, and

Ob.

L.H. *p colla voce*

PIC

gave his arm to lead her to the floor, I

poco rit.

111 **Vivace**

said to him:"You did it! You did it! You

poco *cresc.*

PIC

did it!" They thought she was ec-sta-tic And so damn'd a-ris-to-cra-tic, And they

poco *a* *poco* *mf* *cresc.*

119

PIC

nev-er knew that you did it!

Brass

f *ff* *p*

126 HIGGINS: Thank heavens for Zoltan Karpathy. If it weren't for him I would have
Str.
stacc.
died of boredom. He was there, all right. And up to his old tricks.
Mrs. PEARCE: Karpathy?
134
That dreadful Hungarian? Was he there? HIGGINS: Yes.
Higgins
That
144 Quasi recitativo
HIG
black-guard who u-ses the sci-ence of speech more to black-mail and swin-dle than teach
He
mp Str. trem.
W.W.
ff Brass
(Spoken) "to find out who this Miss Doolittle is"
HIG
made it the dev-il-ish bus-'ness of his...
mp
sfz

149 Vivace

HIG

Ev-'ry time we looked a-round, There he was, that hair-y hound from

p Str.

HIG

Bu-da-pest. ___

mf Brass

Vln.

157

Nev-er leav-ing

p

HIG

us a-lone; Nev-er have I ev-er known a rud-er pest! ___

HIG

Brass

mf

Vln.

165

Fin'l-ly I de-cid-ed it was

W.W.

p

HIG

fool-ish not to let him have his chance with her. ___

Tutti

mf

173
HIG
So I stepped a - side and let him dance with her.
p
ff
180 Misterioso - rubato
Ooz-ing charm from ev-'ry pore, He oiled his way a-round the floor.
Ev - 'ry trick that he could play, He used to strip her mask a - way. And
when at last the dance was done, He glowed as if he knew he'd won!
186 Poco meno
accel.
And with a voice too ea-ger, And a smile too broad, He an -
sf
p Str. trem.
colla voce
accel.

Mrs PEARCE
No!
HIGGINS
Yavol!
HIG
-nounced to the host-ess That she was a fraud!
sf
f
ff
Higgins
192
"Her Eng-lish is too good," he said "Which clear-ly in-di-
Vln.
Solo
etc.
p Str.
-cates that she is for-eign!"
Solo
Vln.
f Brass
200
"Where-as oth-ers are in-struct-ed in their na-tive lan-guage,
p
Eng-lish peo-ple ar-en't!" "And al-
f

*In the New York production, the sequence between the ⊕ signs was omitted

HIG
ab-so-lute-ly writ-ten on her face!" "She thought I was tak-en in, but ac-tual-ly I
f Tutti
p
nev-er was. How could she de-ceive an-oth-er mem-ber of her race?" "I know each
lan-guage on the map!' said he; "and she's Hun-gar-ian as the
First Hun-gar-ian Rhap-so-dy!"
Grave
The Servants
S
A
CHO
T
B
Bra-vo! Bra-vo! Bra-vo!
Bra-vo! Bra-vo! Bra-vo!
mf
Trbn.
Tutti
f
sfz

Allegro con spirito
CHO
Con-grat-u-la - tions, Pro-fes - sor Hig - gins! For your glo - ri - ous vic - to -
Con-grat-u-la - tions, Pro-fes - sor Hig - gins! For your glo - ri - ous vic - to -
Vln.
etc.
f Tutti
his - to -
-ry! Con-grat-u-la-tions, Pro-fes-sor Hig-gins! You'll be men-tioned in his -
-ry! Con-grat-u-la-tions, Pro-fes-sor Hig-gins! You'll be men-tioned in his -
Trpt.
sf f
-ry!
Vivace
Sop. mf
Alto
-t'ry! Con-grat-u-la - tions, Pro-fes - sor Hig - gins! For your
Ten. mf
-t'ry! Con-grat-u-la - tions, Pro-fes - sor Hig - gins! For your
Pickering and one servant
f
This ev-'ning, sir, you did it! You did it! You did it! You said that you would
accel.
Vivace
mf

CHO
glo - ri - ous vic - to - ry! Con-grat-u-la - tions, Pro-fes-sor Hig - gins!
glo - ri - ous vic - to - ry! Con-grat-u-la - tions, Pro-fes-sor Hig - gins!
P & S
do it and in - deed you did! This ev-'ning, sir, you did it! You did it! You did it! We
poco cresc.
poco
CHO
Sing a hail and hal - le - lu - ia; Ev-'ry bit of cred-it for it
Sing a hail and hal - le - lu - ia; Ev-'ry bit of cred-it for it
P & S
know that we have said it, But you did it and the cred-it for it all be -
a poco
mf
cres -
CHO
all be - longs to you!
all be - longs to you!
P & S
- longs to you!
- cen - do
f Tutti
sf
sf
(Dialogue continues)
8....:

No. 20

REPRISE — (Eliza)

"JUST YOU WAIT"

Cue: HIGGINS: Damn Mrs. Pearce! Damn the coffee! And damn you! And damn my own folly in having lavished my hard-earned knowledge and the treasure of my regard and intimacy on a heartless guttersnipe! *(He crashes into the table, setting the recording machine going; hears the "vowels" and snaps it off, and marches out.*

No. 20A

REPRISE—(Freddy)

"ON THE STREET WHERE YOU LIVE"

FRED
57
some-how you are near! The o - ver-pow-er-ing
Cello
Bsn.
Str., W.W.
FRED
feel - ing That an-y sec-ond you may sud-den-ly ap - pear. Peo-ple
Ob.
p Str.
FREDDY: (Spoken) Darling!
ELIZA: What are you doing here?
FREDDY: Nothing. I spend most of my time here. Oh, don't
65
FRED
stop and stare. They don't....
Cello
pp
laugh at me, Miss Doolittle, but this is the only place...
73
ELIZA: Freddy, you don't think I'm a heartless guttersnipe, do you?
FREDDY: Oh, no, darling. How could
you imagine such a thing? You know how I feel. I've written you two and three times a day telling you. Sheets and sheets. Eliza.
Poco moderato
79
p

SONG—(Eliza)(with Freddy)
"SHOW ME"

Chappell

102
furiously
ELIZ
1. Don't talk of stars burn-ing a-bove. If you're in
2. Sing me no song! Read me no rhyme! Don't waste my
p subito
love, Show me! Tell me no dreams
time; Show me! Please don't im-plore,
110
mf
sf
p
filled with de-sire. If you're on fire, Show me!
beg or be-seech. Don't make a speech— Show me!
118
Here we are to-geth-er in the mid-dle of the night! Don't talk of
Nev-er do I ev-er want to hear an-oth-er word. There is-n't
sfp
W.W.

126

LIZ

Spring! Just hold me tight! Any-one who's ev-er
one I have-n't heard. Here we are to-geth-er

W.W.

f *sfp*

LIZ

been in love-'ll tell you that This is no time for a chat!
in what ought to be a dream; Say one more word and I'll scream!

f

134

LIZ

Have-n't your lips longed for my
Have-n't your arms hungered for

p subito

LIZ

touch? Don't say how much; Show me!
mine? Please don't ex-pl'in; Show me!

mf *sf* *sf*

142
ELIZ
Show me! Don't talk of love last - ing through
Show me! Don't wait un - til wrin - kles and
sf sf
time. Make me no un - dy - ing vow.
lines Pop out all ov - er my brow.
150
Show
Show
cresc.
f
sf
me now.
me
1
ff
2
now.
FREDDY: Darling!
Darling! (Curtain)
ff
sf
attacca

No 21

MALE CHORUS–(with Solo, Eliza)

"THE FLOWER MARKET"

Second Cockney (TENOR)
With one e - nor-mous chair Oh, would - n't it be lov-er-ly?
mf

27 Several Cockneys
p
T
T
CHO
Lots of choc-late for me to eat; Lots of coal mak-in' lots of heat;
p
B
B
Lots of choc-late for me to eat; Lots of coal mak-in' lots of heat;
W.W. 8va
Str.
etc.
p

(Eliza has appeared)
Oh, would - n't it be lov-er-ly?
CHO
Warm face, warm hands, warm feet Oh, Ah, lov-er-ly?
Warm face, warm hands, warm feet Oh, Ah, lov-er-ly?

CHO

Oh, so lov-er-ly sit-tin' ab-so-bloom-in'-lute - ly still!

Oh, so lov-er-ly sit-tin' ab-so-bloom-in'-lute - ly still!

p sempre

CHO

I would nev - er budge till Spring crept ov-er me win-der-sill.

I would nev - er budge till Spring crept ov-er me win-der-sill.

Str.

43

CHO

Some - one's head rest - in' on my knee; Warm and ten - der as she can be,

Some - one's head rest - in' on my knee; Warm and ten - der as she can be,

etc.

CHO
Who takes good care of me, Oh, would - n't it be lov-er-ly?
Who takes good care of me, Oh, would - n't it lov-er-ly?
W.W.
tr

FIRST COCKNEY: Good morning, miss. Can I help you?
ELIZA: Do you mind if I warm my hands?
SECOND COCKNEY: Go right ahead, miss.
W.W.
etc.
pp
Str.

ELIZA: Yes?
THIRD COCKNEY: Excuse me, miss. For a second there I thought you was somebody else.
ELIZA: Who?

THIRD COCKNEY: Forgive me, ma'am. Early morning light playing tricks with my eyes.
SECOND COCKNEY: Can I get you a taxi, ma'am? A lady like you shouldn't be
Fl.
60

walkin' around London alone at this hour of the mornin'.
ELIZA: No...Thank you.
FIRST COCKNEY: Good morning, miss.

Eliza picks up a bunch of violets from the basket
espr.
mf
68 Eliza
Some-one's head rest-ing on my knee; Warm and ten-der as he can be,
Ob.
pp
ELIZ
Who takes good care of me Oh, would-n't it be lov-er-ly?
76
Fl.
Cello
Lov-er-ly! Lov-er-ly! Lov-er-ly! Lov-er-ly!
poco rall.
Vln.
più rit.
pp
Dialogue continues

No. 22 SONG– (Doolittle) and Chorus (with Solo, Harry)

"GET ME TO THE CHURCH ON TIME"

Cue: FREDDY: Are you all finished here?
ELIZA: Yes, Freddy. I'm all finished here. Good luck, Dad
JAMIE: Come along, Alfie.

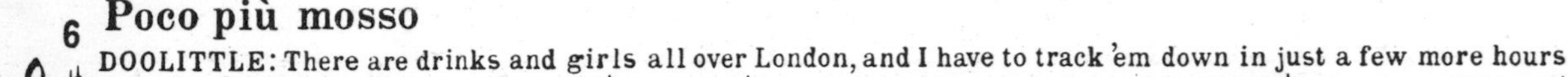

DOOLITTLE: How much time
(Spoken) do I have left?

6
Poco più mosso
DOOLITTLE: There are drinks and girls all over London, and I have to track 'em down in just a few more hours.

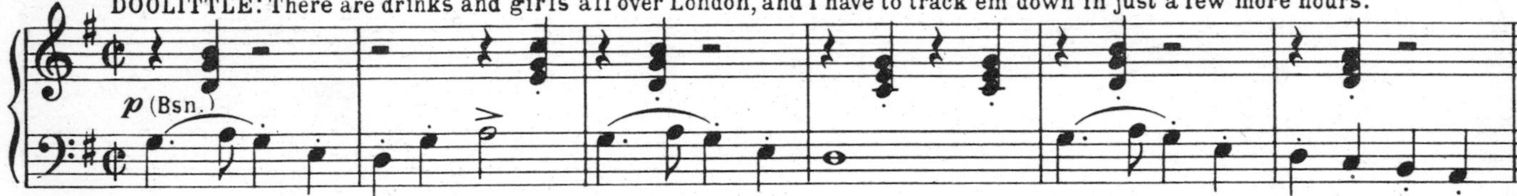

Doolitte

DOO
Let's have a whop-per, But get me to the church on time!
28
I got-ta be there in the mor-nin', Spruced up and
Hn.
look-in' in me prime.
36
Girls, come and kiss me,
Show how you'll miss me, But get me to the church on time!
(Trpt.)
44
If I am dan-cin,' Roll up the floor. If I am
(Trbn.)

52
DOO
whist - lin', Whewt me out the door! For I'm get - tin' mar-ried in the
mor - nin'. Ding, dong! the bells are gon-na chime.
(Trpt W.W.)
(Trpt W.W.)
60
Kick up a rum - pus, But don't lose the com - pass; And get me to the
sf
sf
68
church, Get me to the church. For Gawd's sake, get me to the
church on time!
(Bells)
cresc.
f
rall.
ff

76
Allegro commodo
DOO
I'm get - tin' mar - ried in the mor - nin'.
Ding, dong! the
S
A
CHO
T
B
mf (Str. Hn.)
Trpt.
bells are gon-na chime!
84
Drug me or jail me, Stamp me and
mail me. But get me to the church on time.

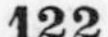

92

DOO: I got - ta be there in the mor - nin' Spruced up and

CHO: I got - ta be there in the mor - nin' Spruced up and

I got - ta be there in the mor - nin' Spruced up and

Hn.

DOO: look-in' in my prime. Some bloke who's ab - le Lift up the

CHO: look-in' in my prime.

look-in' in my prime.

sf

DOO: ta - ble. And get me to the church on time. *mp* If I am

CHO: And get me to the church on time. *mp* If I am

mp And get me to the church on time.

Tutti

mp

108

DOO: fly - in', then shoot me down. If I am woo - in', Get her out of

CHO: fly - in', then shoot me down.

Ah, down.

Then shoot me down.

(Trpts.) (Trbns.) *p* *p*

116 *mf*

DOO: town! For I'm get - tin' mar-ried in the mor - nin'.

CHO: For I'm get - tin' mar-ried in the mor - nin'.

For I'm get - tin' mar-ried in the mor - nin'.

Trpt. *più f*

cresc.

DOO: Ding, dong! The bells are gon - na chime!

CHO: Ding, dong! The bells are gon - na chime!

Ding, dong! The bells are gon - na chime!

(Trpt. W.W.) Hn.

124
DOO
Feath - er and tar me, Call out the Ar-my; But get me to the church,
p sub.
sf
sf
mf
f
For Gawd's sake, get me to the church on
poco accel. e cresc.
CHO
Get me to the church,
f
f
(Bells)
poco accel. e cresc.
136 Street Can-Can
Allegro molto con brio
time
The crowd "pulls out the stopper" and dances a wild street dance.
f
(Tutti)
144
sf

152
160
168
mf
f
sf
sf
sf

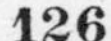

176

sf

184

cresc.

192

mf subito

200

(Tap steps)

sf

208

216
p
sf
f
(Trbn.)
ff
224
sf
(Cymb.)
232
W.W.
f (Hn.)
240

L'istesso tempo

ff sempre

(Trbn.)

molto marc.

256 (W.W. Vln.)

sf

sf

264 (Trpt.)

(Trbn.)

272 (W.W. Vln.)

sf

280 Vln.

W.W.

(Tutti)

288
ff sempre
(Trbn.)
(Trbn.)
molto marc.
(Tutti)
296
(Tap steps.)
308
ff
ff
sff
8

323 Andante tranquillo
Dawn breaks over the Flower Market
327
Harry
Star - light is
Soprano
Alto
Hmm,
Tenor
Bass
Hmm,
CHO
Str.W.W.
poco rit.
Hn.
a tempo
HAR
reel-in' home to bed now.
Mor - nin' is smear-in' up the
Hmm,
Hmm,
Hp.
335
cresc.
sky.
Lon - don is wak-in', Day - light is
Hp.Hn.
Hn.
Hp.

Molto moderato
HAR
CHO
break-in'; Good luck, old chum. Good health, good - - bye.
mf
pp
Cl.
Bsn.
p
Doolittle
I'm get-tin' mar-ried in the mor - nin'. Ding, dong! the bells are gon-na chime!
Ah,
Str.
accel. poco a poco
Hn.
accel. e cresc.
W.W.
DOO
accel. e cresc. poco a poco
Hail and sa - lute me, Then haul off and boot me. And
Ah,
f
Tutti

Chappell

355 Allegro con brio
ff
get me to the church, get me to the church, For Gawd's sake, get me to the church on time.
CHO
(f)
cresc.
church, For Gawd's sake, get me to the church on
church, For Gawd's sake, get me to the church on
sfz
time.
ff
attacca

No. 23

CHANGE OF SCENE

Nº 24 SONG — (Higgins, with Pickering)

"A HYMN TO HIM"

Cue: PICKERING: (*telephoning*) Now, see here, my good man, I'm not at all pleased with the tenor of that question. What the girl does here is our affair. Your affair is to get her back so she can continue doing it

25
Whitehall seven,
two, double four, please
33 Higgins
Wom-en are ir-rat-ion-al, that's
HIG
all there is to that! Their heads are full of cot-ton, hay, and rags! They're
Trpt.
Trpt.
41
noth-ing but ex-as-per-at-ing, ir-ri-tat-ing, va-cil-lat-ing, cal-cu-lat-ing,
ag-i-tat-ing, Mad-den-ing, and in-fur-i-at-ing hags!
49

PICKERING: (telephoning) Brewster Budgin, please........
Yes, I'll wait.
Poco meno
Cl.
mp
Vln.
HIGGINS: Pickering why can't a woman be more like a man? Yes,
59 Tempo di marcia
Why can't a wo-man be more like a man? Men are so
sf Tutti
f
Str. W.W.
HIG
hon-est, so thor-ough-ly square; E-ter-nal-ly no-ble,
67
Trpt.
his-tor-ic-'ly fair; Who, when you win, will al-ways give your back a
pat. Why can't a wo-man be like that?
Brass
sf
Tutti
ff

79

HIG

Why does ev - 'ry - one do what the oth - ers do? Can't a wo - man

p Str. Hn. Str.

learn to use her head?

87

Why do they do ev - 'ry-thing their

Trbn.

moth - ers do? Why don't they grow up like their fa - ther in - stead?

mf

95

Why can't a wo - man take af - ter a man? Men are so

p

pleas - ant, so eas - y to please; When - ev - er you're with them,

Trpt

PICKERING: Of course not.
107
HIG
you're al-ways at ease. Would you be slight-ed if I did-n't speak for hours?
Higgins
PICKERING: Nonsense.
Higgins
Would you be liv-id if I had a drink or two? Would you be wound-ed if I
PICKERING: Never!
118 Higgins
HIG
nev-er sent you flow-ers? Why can't a wo-man be like you?
Brass
Tutti
sf
ff
123
HIG
One man in a mil-lion may shout a bit.
Hn.
sfz
p Str.
131
HIG
Now and then there's one with slight de-fects; One, per-haps, whose
Str.
Trbn.

HIG
truth - ful-ness you doubt a bit. But by and large we are a mar - vel-lous sex!
mf
139
Why can't a wo - man be-have like a man? Men are so
p
friend-ly, good nat-ured and kind. A bet-ter com - pan-ion
Trpt.
147
you nev-er will find. If I were hours late for din - ner, would you
PICKERING:
Of course not.
Higgins
155
bel - low? If I for - got your sil - ly birth - day, would you fuss?
PICKERING:
Nonsense.

Higgins
PICKERING: Never!
162
Higgins
Would you com - plain if I took out an-oth - er fel-low?
Why can't a
sf
HIG
wo-man be like us.
Tutti
ff
ff
sf

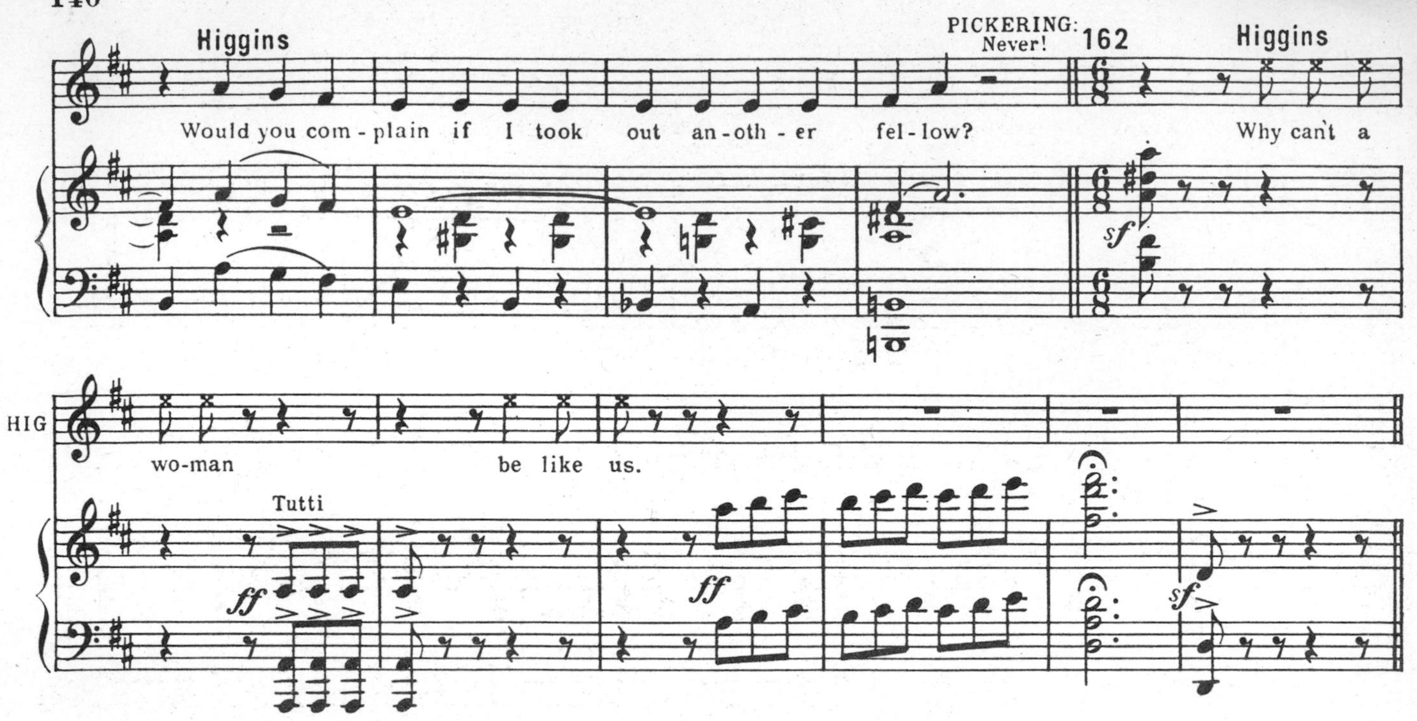

PICKERING: (*telephoning*) Hello, is Brewster Budgin there, please?
(*Dialogue continues*)
Cue: HIGGINS: You see that, Mrs. Pearce. I'm disturbed and he runs to help. Now there's a good fellow. Mrs. Pearce, you're a woman,

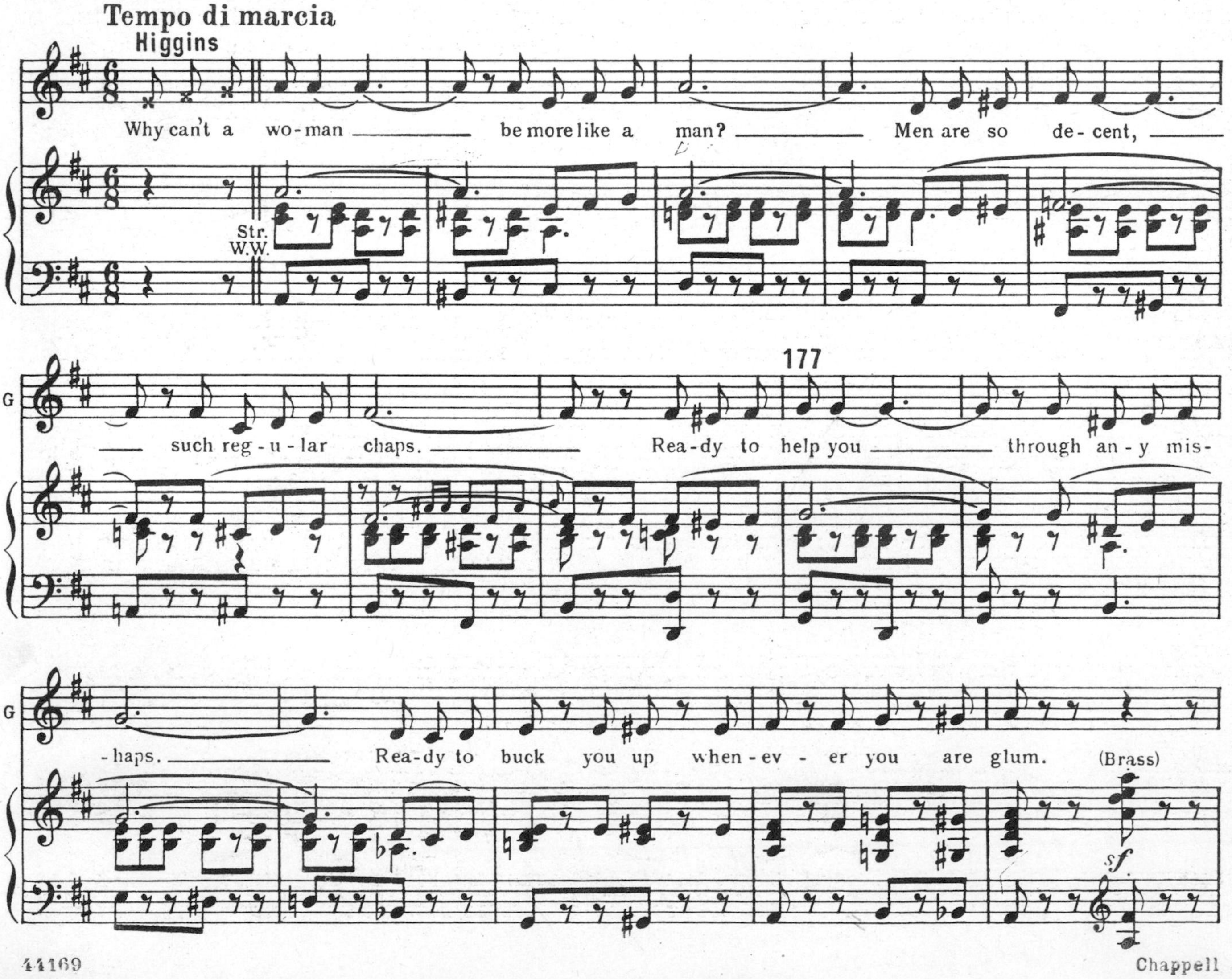

Tempo di marcia
Higgins
Why can't a wo-man be more like a man? Men are so de-cent,
Str.
W.W.
HIG
such reg-u-lar chaps. Rea-dy to help you through an-y mis-
177
HIG
-haps. Rea-dy to buck you up when-ev - er you are glum.
(Brass)
sf

HIG

Why can't a wo-man be a chum?

Tutti

sf *ff*

189

Why is think - ing some - thing wo - men nev - er do? Why is log - ic

p Str. Hn. Str.

nev - er ev - en tried?

Trbn.

197

Straight - 'ning up their hair is all they

ev - er do. Why don't they straight - en up the mess that's in - side?

mf

205

Why can't a wo-man be more like a man? If I were a

p

HIG

wo-man ——— who'd been to a ball, ——— Been hailed as a prin-cess ———

HIG

——— by one and by all; ——— Would I start weep-ing like a bath-tub o-ver-

217

HIG

-flow-ing? And car-ry on as if my home were in a tree? Would I run

HIG

off and nev-er tell me where I'm go-ing? Why can't a wo-man

228

ff

Curtain
HIG
be like me?
f
ff
sf
attacca
Nº 24a
CHANGE OF SCENE
Brilliante
ff Tutti
7
Hn.
W. W.
dim.
13
mf
Str., W.W.
Mrs. HIGGINS
And you mean to say that ....
(Dialogue continues)
W.W.
mp
p
Bsn., Hn

No. 25. SONG: (Eliza) (with Higgins)

"WITHOUT YOU"

Cue: ELIZA: Wring away! What do I care? I knew you'd strike me one day. Aha, that's done you, 'enry 'iggins, it 'as. Now I don't care that— for your bullying and your big talk.

13 HIGGINS: You impudent hussy! There isn't an idea in your head or a word in your mouth that I haven't put there!

Eliza

There'll be

pp Str. *rit.* Harp

17 Allegro con moto

ELIZ

spring ev-'ry year with-out you. Eng-land still will be here with-out you. There'll be fruit on the tree; And a shore by the sea; There'll be crum-pets and tea with-out you.

Bells · Cello *p* · add Fl., Cl.

25

Art and mu-sic will thrive with-out you. Some-how Keats will sur-vive with-out you. And there

Cello *p* · Bells

ELIZ

still will be rain on that plain down in Spain, E-ven that will re-main with-out

add Fl., Cl.

ELIZ

you. I can do ______ with-out you.

mf Trpt.

Str., Cl.

36

ELIZ

You, dear friend, who talk so well,

Str., W.W.

p

etc.

ELIZ

You can go to Hert-ford, Her-e-ford and Hamp-shire.— They can

f Trpt. *p* Cello

44
ELIZ
still rule the land with-out you. ——— Wind-sor Cas - tle will stand with-out you. ——— And with-

f *p* *f* *p*

HIGGINS: You brazen hussy!

Eliza

ELIZ
-out much a-do We can all mud-dle through with-out you. With-

mf dim. *p*

52 **Poco meno**

ELIZ
-out your pull-ing it, the tide comes in, With - out your twirl-ing it, the earth can spin. With-

p Trbn. *sf* *p* *sf*

Giusto

ELIZ
-out your push-ing them, the clouds roll by. If they can do with-out you, duck-y so can I! I shall

p *poco rall.* *sf* > *p* Trbn. Cello

60

ELIZ: not feel a-lone with-out you. I can stand on my own with-out

f Trpt. *p*

ELIZ: you. —— So go back in your shell, I can *poco rit.* do blood-y well with-out — **Higgins** By

Vln. *p* *poco rit.*

Vivace

HIG: George, I real-ly did it! I did it! I did it! I said I'd make a

pp

HIG: wom-an and in-deed I did! I knew that I could do it! I knew it! I

HIG: knew it! I said I'd make a wom-an and suc-ceed I did!

(Spoken): Eliza, you're magnificent!

pp *Dialogue continues*

No. 26

SONG—(Higgins)

"I'VE GROWN ACCUSTOMED TO HER FACE"

Cue: HIGGINS : She's an owl sickened by a few days of my sunshine! Very well! Let her go! I can do without her! I can do without anybody! I have my own soul! My own spark of divine fire!
Mrs. HIGGINS : Bravo —— Eliza! *(Curtain)*

Furioso
ff Tutti
sfz
8
(The curtain rises)
16 Higgins (entering in great rage)
poco rall.
Damn!!
Damn!!
Damn!!
Damn!! I've grown accustomed to her face!
Str.
mf
f cantabile
Moderato con tenerezza
HIG
She al-most makes the day be-gin.
I've grown ac -
Cl.

HIG
-cus-tomed to the tune She whis-tles night and noon. Her smiles, her frowns, her
colla voce
28
ups, her downs Are sec-ond na-ture to me now; Like breath-ing out and breath-ing in.
I was se - rene-ly in-de-pend-ent and con-tent be-fore we met;
Hp.
Sure-ly I could al-ways be that way a-gain and yet I've grown ac - cus-tomed to her looks; Ac-
Solo Vln.
pp
p
-cus-tomed to her voice: Ac - cus-tomed to her face.
f W.W.
rit.

HIGGINS: Marry Freddy! What an infantile idea! What a heartless, wicked, brainless thing to do. But she'll regret it. It's doomed before they even take the vow!

65
HIG
Beg-ging for her bread and wa - ter, While her hus-band has his
poco rit.
cresc.
break-fast in bed! In a
73
Meno mosso
year or so, when she's
Tutti
sf
mp
pre - ma - ture - ly grey, And the blos-som in her cheek has turned to chalk,
mf
She'll come home, and lo! He'll have upped and run a - way, With a
81
p
so - cial climb - ing heir - ess from New York! Poor E - li - za!
89
Quasi recitativo
Tutti
mf

HIG
How simp-ly fright-ful! How hu-mil-i-at-ing! How de-
-light-ful!
Solo Vln.
mf
97 Allegro molto
a piacere
Str.
pp
HIGGINS:
How poignant it will be on that inevitable
night when she hammers on my door in tears and rags. Miserable and lonely, repentant and
105
Cl.
contrite. Will I let her in or hurl her to the wolves? Give her kindness, or
Vln.
113
the treatment she deserves? Will I take her back or throw the baggage
W.W.

Tranquillo
120
HIG
out? I'm a most forgiving man, The sort who nev - er could, ev - er would
Cl.
Harp
Str.
Take a pos-i-tion and staunch-ly nev-er budge. Just a most for-giv-ing man.
Cl.
Str.
Allegro vivo
But I shall nev-er take her back!
Ob.
mf
Str.
f Trpt.
If she were crawl-ing on her knees!
W.W.
mf
135
Let her prom-ise to a - tone! Let her shi - ver, Let her moan! I will

HIG
slam the door and let the hell-cat freeze!
W.W.Trpt.
ff
Marry Freddy!
Ha!
ten.
ten.
ten.
149
Appassionato e rubato
f
Hn.
dim. molto
p
dim.
Moderato con tenderezza
Higgins
HIG
But I'm so used to hear her say, "Good morn-ing" ev-'ry day. Her
Str.
pp
156
HIG
joys, her woes, Her highs, her lows, Are sec-ond na-ture to me now;
HIG
Like breath-ing out and breath-ing in. I'm ver-y

HIG

grate - ful she's a wom - an And so eas - y to for - get;

Harp

HIG

Rath - er like a hab - it One can al - ways break and yet, I've grown ac -

poco rit.

Vln. solo

HIG

-cus-tomed to the trace Of some-thing in the air; Ac - cus-tomed to her face.

morendo

pp *cresc. molto*

Tutti

Curtain

W.W. Brass

169 L'istesso tempo

Vln. Hn.

ff

f molto cantabile

simile

The scene has changed
177
Higgins enters
He slowly looks about his empty room.
poco calmando
a tempo
He turns on the recording machine
Solo Vln.
mp
pp tranquillo
Tempo rubato
189
Eliza's recorded voice is heard:
I want to be a lady in a flower shop instead
Harp
of sellin' flowers at the corner of Tottenham Court Road. But they won't take me unless I talk more genteel.
He said he could teach me. Well here I am ready to pay...
Eliza enters and stands by the recording machine, listening.

197
.....not askin' any favour and he treats me as if I was dirt. I know what lessons cost, and I'm ready to pay.
HIGGINS' VOICE: It's almost irresistible. She's so deliciously low, so horribly dirty.
rit. e morendo
She switches off the recording machine
ELIZA: I washed my face and hands before I came, I did.
HIGGINS: (stretching back on his stool and pulling his hat down over his eyes) Eliza? Where the devil are my slippers?
lunga
Molto maestoso
ff (Tutti)
(Curtain)
204
(Brass)
ffz
fff

Nº 27 MUSIC FOR CURTAIN CALLS

No.28

EXIT MUSIC

29
Trbn.
mf Brass
Hp. gliss.
49
8va
8va
Br.
f sempre
57 Moderato
Cello
65

73
Cello
81
Cls.
Vln.
89
Tutti
3
97
Cello Bsn.
Ob. espr.
105
Cello
113

123 Allegro vivo
f
Tutti
131
139
147
155

Lowe and Brydone (Printers) Limited, London